introduction

In selecting the pictures for this book two things soon became apparent. Firstly, how could I do justice to mountaineering, not only in a worldwide sense but also in my home country of Scotland and the UK — with just 40 pictures. "Impossible", was my immediate reaction. Buying images provided one solution but in terms of personal achievement that would have been unsatisfactory. In any case this seemed like an excuse for not travelling — my second point. I consider myself to have been in a very privileged position with my work as a mountain guide and my work within TV and film, both of which have taken me to some amazing places. But the bottom line was that in order to expand my library I would have to travel more. Selecting forty worldwide pictures therefore proved to be something of a challenge. For example, I was uncomfortably aware of my solitary, token picture of climbing in Northumberland as justification for 'British' status. There again we've seen a lot of quality images from England and Wales recently so I didn't feel so bad, but what about Ireland…and the Himalaya — arrgh! I also did not want this book to come across as being too elitist and yet the images were to be inspirational, have wide appeal and contain a fair number of classic climbs. With assurance and the aid of my clear thinking wife, I finally let go. Now when I look at the book in its neat and concise, complete form, I actua'' ''''''''''''' travel again — dare I say so myself! Travelling (expands our minds. Given the opportunity eve Our passion for climbing and an appreciation (provide a means, a reasoning, or if you like, which to achieve our dreams.

Cubby.

Mont Blanc (4807m) and the Peuterey Ridge.
Sunrise over the Italian side of Europe's highest mountain. The magnificent profile of the Peuterey is one of the most sought after classic ridges in the Alps and unlike the 'Voie Normale', you certainly won't be queuing up on this one!

Leo Holding going for it on Tsunami, Teplici, Czech Republic.

"You like Tsunami....yes. How far deed you take fall...fifteen metre, mmm...not bad. But you must drink more beer!" I think we've gone soft in the west! Sport climbing in the Czech Republic differs from the west, placing emphasis on fall potential as much as difficulty! Large door knocker-like bolts are used very sparingly. These are supplemented with knotted slings which are jammed into cracks like "Rocks", thereby minimising erosion.

For those operating in the realms of E5 or above, the stupendous wall of Rora Head, only a kilometre to the south of The Old Man of Hoy, offers a triptych of outstanding routes, the original and most amenable being Mucklehouse Wall.

Cut Throat R.H Finish (V), Beinn Udlaidh
Drip, drip, drip....... mmm, think I'll leave the Direct for another day. Spectacular icicles on Scotland's premier ice climbing venue.

Mark Diggins approaches the magnificent South Face of Proboscis, illuminated by the early morning light. Cirque of the Unclimbables, North West Territories.

Sadie Renwick on High Pitched Scream, a classic 7a at Weem Rocks.

The Midi Plan Traverse on the Chamonix aiguilles and descent via the Mer de Glace is one of the great classics of the Alps.

Julian Lines gets his fix on the wonderfully sculptured granite of Capo Testa, Sardinia.

Mid April and winter returns with a vengeance. The leader is buffeted by high winds and blinding spindrift on Fingers Ridge, a classic grade IV in the Cairngorms.

Where others might consider Brad Pitt, or even Joe Simpson as role models, Himalayan veteran Steven Venables gets closer to where it all began — The Matterhorn - and reincarnates himself as Edward Whymper. Make sure you keep a diary!

Running it out above the delectable crux slab of Ardverikie Wall Hard Severe, Binnein Shuas. A climb beautifully dubbed by the great Scottish mountaineer and personality, Tom Patey as, "the best climb that I never did".

Chris Dale waves a victory salute from the top of Dun Dubh in the Quiraing on the Isle of Skye. Chris claims this to be the last unclimbed "green" summit in the British Isles – any takers!

Controversy in the making — Neil Gresham attempts to 'red-point' the first ascent of Tempest, X.9, Glen Coe.

A traverse of Jordan's Jebel Rum by utilising two Bedouin climbs, Sabbah's Route and Hammad's Route, and exiting by Lawrence of Arabia's Well, is without doubt one of the great mountaineering excursions of the world. Composed entirely of sandstone, the complex rock architecture is sure to test anyone's route finding skills – a local guide shows the way!

Bitter winter winds sweep the spectacular Dent du Geant, Mont Blanc Massif, France.

Prore - an atmospheric VS in the Northern Cairngorms, rather uncharacteristically seen here without a plating of snow and ice.

Never go out in winter without an ice axe and always ensure that you are well prepared and suitably clad!

Climatic change isn't just confined to the UK. A climber pulls gingerly onto a dripping free standing icicle, Argentiere, Haute Savoie, France.

Just inside the Arctic circle on the west coast of Norway, lies a group of islands known as Lofoten. These magical islands present a number of superb granite slabs, big walls and lots of bouldering, all in a lovely setting and of course the summer sun never dips below the horizon. Mick Fowler and Mark Garthwaite on the first ascent of the appropriately named, 'Cup of Tea', E4 – a 2000 foot route on The Priest.

Deep in the afforested hills overlooking the sleepy Perthshire town of Old Dunkeld, a rudely overhanging buttress of perfect mica schist hosts one of Scotland's most sought after 7c's, Hamish Teds Excellent Adventure. Tracy Harrison approaches the celebrated crux egyptian.

What constitutes a world-class climb? Sixteen pitches of south-facing peerless granite, breathtaking views of the Bernese Oberland, just over an hours approach and at the end of the day a restaurant with one of the best wine lists in the Swiss Alps. On the penultimate pitch of Motorhead, VII- (E2 5c), Eldorado, Switzerland.

Sunlit cornices threaten the approach to Gardyloo Gully, Ben Nevis. The gully was named such because of the rubbish discarded by occupants of the summit observatory, which was built in 1883 and was in existence for 17 years until its closure in 1904.

Grey Panther, E1 5b. Stemming the pleats on a suitably named Kilt Rock on the Isle of Skye.

At 5500 metres above the Siula Glacier in the Cordillera Huayhuash, Peru, Simon Yates reinvents himself for the making of the film, Touching The Void.

A different view of Ben Lomond – one of the most popular munros on the west coast of Scotland. At E8, the same can't be said of Dalriada which follows the spectacular profile of Baillie's Overhang on the North Peak of the Cobbler.

In a crevasse somewhere beneath the Monchjoch! This is normally the starting point for the big three Oberland giants, the Jungfrau, Monche and Eiger.

Ibex are natural born climbers, although this one, seen outside the Cabane D'Orny in Switzerland, is something of a permanent fixture!

High above a sea of cloud, two climbers can be seen on the final stages of Tower Ridge, Ben Nev

Overhanging Crack, E2 5c. Local lass, Karin Magog on-sighting this notorious County classic, but just how much preparation is required to attempt such a reasonable climb (by Northumberland standards). Only days previously Karin red-pointed her first 8a+ but that smile after doing the Crack said it all!

Bouldering on the superb sculptured granite at Mount Teidi National Park – Tenerife is not only about clubbing!

Archetypal Scottish winter mixed climbing – The Crack, VII, Northern Cairngorms.

"Quel pays, uno caramelo". Sometimes it's difficult to imagine life in other parts of the world. 'Nina' and an elder from a remote mountain village near Cajatambo, situated at an elevation of nearly 4000 metres in the Cordillera Hauyhuash, Peru.

The Screaming Ab Dabs, E6 – in other words, the sort of stuff that nightmares are made of! To the dedicated rock climber however, the Atlantic washed gneiss on the west coast of Lewis in the Outer Hebrides offers some of the most spectacular textured quality rock in the British Isles.

The Totem Pole in Tasmania is an incredible monolith, a must do for any capable aspiring rock climber embarking on a world tour. But hurry while it still stands! Steve Monks approaches the 5.12a crux.

It's difficult to comprehend the mental and physical commitment required to attempt a new line of this calibre in 1960. Put yourself in their boots! A Hawser laid rope tied around the waist, a few ex W.D krabs, slings, pitons and a couple of metal spikes they called ice pegs. Then imagine wielding a single wooden shafted axe, hacking and cutting steps for hours on end. One can only marvel. Smiths Route, V, Ben Nevis.

There's no substitute for raw power. Malcolm Smith dispenses with the second ascent of this F8a+, Sabotage, Dumbarton Rock, Scotland.

The French certainly have style! This plaque has been lovingly installed to indicate the start of a 7c at Sugiton, The Calanques in France.

name:

address:

tel (1): tel (2):

e-mail:

name:

address:

tel (1): tel (2):

e-mail:

name:

address:

tel (1): tel (2):

e-mail:

name:

address:

tel (1): tel (2):

e-mail:

name:

address:

tel (1): tel (2):

e-mail:

name:

address:

tel (1): tel (2):

e-mail:

name:

address:

tel (1):   tel (2):

e-mail:

name:

address:

tel (1):   tel (2):

e-mail:

name:

address:

tel (1):   tel (2):

e-mail:

name:

address:

tel (1):   tel (2):

e-mail:

name:

address:

tel (1):   tel (2):

e-mail:

name:

address:

tel (1):   tel (2):

e-mail:

name:

address:

tel (1):   tel (2):

e-mail:

name:

address:

tel (1):   tel (2):

e-mail:

name:

address:

tel (1):   tel (2):

e-mail:

name:

address:

tel (1):   tel (2):

e-mail:

name:

address:

tel (1):   tel (2):

e-mail:

name:

address:

tel (1):   tel (2):

e-mail:

name:

address:

tel (1):   tel (2):

e-mail:

name:

address:

tel (1):   tel (2):

e-mail:

name:

address:

tel (1):   tel (2):

e-mail:

name:

address:

tel (1):   tel (2):

e-mail:

name:

address:

tel (1):   tel (2):

e-mail:

name:

address:

tel (1):   tel (2):

e-mail:

name:

address:

tel (1):   tel (2):

e-mail:

name:

address:

tel (1):   tel (2):

e-mail:

name:

address:

tel (1):   tel (2):

e-mail:

name:

address:

tel (1):   tel (2):

e-mail:

name:

address:

tel (1):   tel (2):

e-mail:

name:

address:

tel (1):   tel (2):

e-mail:

name:

address:

tel (1):   tel (2):

e-mail:

name:

address:

tel (1):   tel (2):

e-mail:

name:

address:

tel (1):   tel (2):

e-mail:

name:

address:

tel (1):   tel (2):

e-mail:

name:

address:

tel (1):   tel (2):

e-mail:

name:

address:

tel (1):   tel (2):

e-mail:

The MCofS (The Mountaineering Council of Scotland)

The MCofS is the representative body for climbers, walkers, mountaineers and cross-country skiers who enjoy the Scottish mountains.

For more information on news/events, access issues, debates, courses, expedition grants and much more, visit: www.mountaineering-scotland.org.uk tel:01738 638227

The BMC (The British Mountaineering Council)

The BMC is the representative body that exists to protect the freedoms and promote the interest of climbers, hillwalkers and mountaineers, including ski-mountaineers.

For more info on expedition grants and guidelines, guidebooks, access notes, bird restrictions, insurance, news & events and much more, visit this very useful site at: www.thebmc.co.uk tel: 0870 010 4878

The MCI (The Mountaineering Council of Ireland)

The MCI is the representative body for the sport of mountaineering including hill walking, climbing and rambling.

For more info on rock climbing in Ireland, news, events, weather, guidebooks, insurance, clubs and more, visit: www.mountaineering.ie   tel: +353 1 6251115

SMC (Scottish Mountaineering Club) & SMT (Scottish Mountaineering Trust)

The SMC is one of Scotland's oldest private mountaineering Clubs, founded in 1889 and currently has over 400 members. The SMC Journal, which is published annually, records all new Scottish rock and ice climbs.

For more information about the SMC and the SMT series of guidebooks to hill walking and climbing in Scotland, expedition grants and much more, visit: www.smc.org.uk

BMG (British Mountain Guides)

All British Mountain Guides are members of the International Union of Associations of Mountain Guides (IFMGA). This membership, shared at present with guides from sixteen other countries, gives British Guides absolute equivalence with Guides in Alpine countries and throughout the world. The award of the International Guides Carnet demands the highest standards of skill and professionalism in all aspects of mountaineering.

For a full BMG list, details of insurance and more, visit: www.bmg-org.uk

AMI (Association of Mountain Instructors)

The representative body for professionally qualified mountain instructors in the British Isles. For more information on training and assessments for MIC (Mountain Instructor Certificate), MIA (Mountain Instructor Award) and Winter ML (Mountain Leader),

tel: 01690 720314 or visit www.ami.org.uk

MLTB (Mountain Leader Training UK)
For details on training and assessments for SPA(Single Pitch Award), Summer ML(Mountain Leader) and WGL (Walking Group Leader award), tel: 01690 720314 or visit www.mltb.org.uk

SAIS (SportScotland Avalanche Information Service)
Throughout the winter months, the SAIS offers a free avalanche forecasting service for all the major climbing venues in Scotland. Also links to other useful sites, visit: www.sais.gov.uk

HILL PHONES
Set up in 1996, this service offers daily information for hill walkers and climbers about stag stalking activities throughout the Scottish stalking season. Calls are charged at normal rates. Messages are updated daily and forecasts are given for a few days ahead wherever possible. If you don't want a bullet in your back, visit: www.snh.org.uk/hillphones/latest.asp

WEATHER FORECASTS & WEB CAMS
www.mwis.org.uk – expert mountain weather forecasting, one of the best for climbers in the UK.
www.met-office.gov.uk – general forecasts from the Met Office
www.bbc.co.uk/weather - the BBC's general weather forecasts

UK Mountain forecasts - Premium rate (approx. 60p per minute)
West Highlands   09068 500 441
East Highlands   09068 500 442
Lake District   09068 500 484
Snowdonia   09068 500 449

NATIONAL OUTDOOR CENTRES
Plas Y Brenin, North Wales – www.pyb.co.uk or call 01690 720214
Glenmore Lodge, Scotland – www.glenmorelodge.org.uk or call 01479 861256
Tiglin, Ireland – www.tiglin.com or call (0404) 40169

OTHER USEFUL WEBSITES
www.scottishclimbs.com – for news, climbing/bouldering guides, articles, forums, new routes and more.....
www.planetfear.com – for shopping, reviews, forums, news, events, articles, photos and more.....
www.rockfax.com – for climbing publications, climbing areas, databases, forums and more ...
www.ukclimbing.com – the no.1 site for forums plus info on climbing walls, weather forecasts, crag/route databases, news, articles and more......
www.climbinfo.co.uk/links – a lot of useful info with links to endless sites for climbers.

On the giddy heights of the Aiguille du Plan, with the descent onto the backbone of the Mer de Glace a long, long way below. Chamonix, France.

"Mountaineering is but an expression of the basic instinct to explore the unknown.......Since happiness is most often found by those who have learned to live in every moment of the present, none has such prodigal opportunities of attaining that as the traveller.....attainment of a set objective is but a secondary matter, the traveller should not anticipate the journey's end. So long as he loses consciousness of self, and is aware in all his senses of the present scene, almost any part of the world is as good as another. Mountain or desert it is all one".

Tom Longstaff, This My Voyage.

They say that there is no finer sight than a Hebridean sunset. Looking towards the Flannan Isles from the west coast of Lewis. A lighthouse on these remote islands was the scene of an unsolved mystery. In 1900, in foul weather, its three keepers vanished without a trace, leaving oil skins still hanging and a half eaten meal!

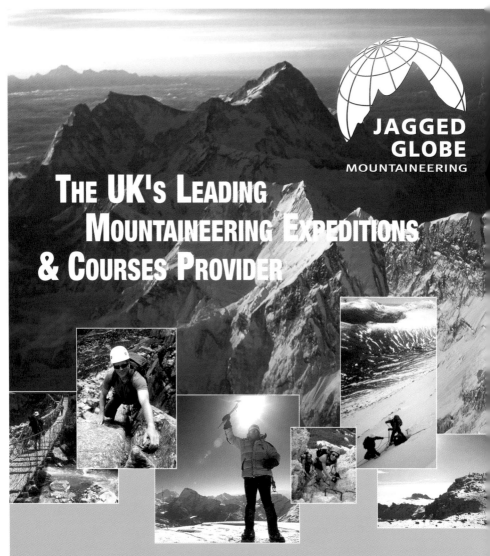

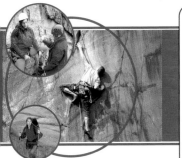